Look and Find
on
the *Night*
Before
Christmas

When Every
Creature Is Stirring!

(with apologies to Clement Moore)

Illustrated by Jerry Tiritilli

Illustration Assistant: Marge Lebak Tiritilli

Illustration Script Development and Poem
by Jane Jerrard

Louis Weber, C.E.O.
Publications International, Ltd.
7373 North Cicero Avenue
Lincolnwood, Illinois 60646

Permission is never granted for commercial purposes.

Manufactured in the U.S.A.

8 7 6 5 4 3 2 1

ISBN 1-56173-421-7

PUBLICATIONS INTERNATIONAL, LTD.

'Twas the night before Christmas
and all through the city
Every creature was stirring—
    the lights were so pretty!
This mouse was out searching
    for Santa with care.
Couldn't risk getting squished
    before I got there.

 My name is A. Mouse, and
I'm out looking for Santa
downtown. Can you
spot me? Can you
help me find Santa Claus?
And while you're at it, see if
you can find these city folks.

Calvin Con Artist   Celia City Slicker

Myra Meter Maid

Peter Pickpocket

Ellen Executive

Tex, the urban cowboy

LADIES' STOCKINGS

SALE ON STUFFED SHIRTS

BILL BILL

SECOND STORY BOOKS

C.D.'S MUSIC STORE

On the night before Christmas,
 the mall is jam-packed.
(No St. Nick in sight—
 he's still filling his sack.)
The parents are shopping,
 the stuff looks entrancing.
Their kids dream of skateboards,
 not sugarplums dancing!

Can you spot me, A. Mouse, and
Santa Claus, too? And can you find
these last-minute shoppers?

Winnie Whiner

Clara the Clothes Horse

Charlie Charge-it

Ms. Gotbucks

Kassie Klepto

Bo the Bargain Hunter

Wanda Window Shopper

BACK IN 5 MIN.

QUICKIE BURGER

DUDS FOR DUDES

TRUNK SALE

SALE

SALE

BATHTIME

LOST AND FOUND

O n the night before Christmas,
what do you think
Is more fun than a party
at an ice-skating rink?
The moon was so bright,
I could see I was near—
For before me I saw
eight skating reindeer!

I know I'm hot on Santa's trail—
even though it's pretty cold here!
Do you see him? And can you find
me and Santa's eight reindeer?

Dasher   Dancer   Prancer

Vixen   Comet   Cupid

Donder   Blitzen

It's the night before Christmas.
  What do animals do?
Only one way to see;
  I snuck into the zoo!
I know Santa is here;
  to his reindeer he's shoutin',
"To the bears in their cage!
  To the seals in the fountain!"

This party's a zoo! After you find Santa and me, A. Mouse, see if you can spot these unusual critters.

A silly goose

A dandy lion

A playin' possum

A holy cow

A bum steer

Leapin' lizards

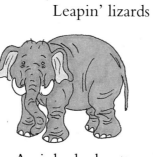

A Christmas seal

A pink elephant

'Twas the Christmas Eve train
from Detroit to Atlanta—
But just one more stop
for me and old Santa.
Down the smokestack he went,
dressed in red head to foot,
But he came out all dusty
and covered with soot.

Can you find Santa? Then look for
me and these other passengers.

The Sundance Kid

Chuck Chatterbox

Casey Jones

Connie Conductor

Peter Pullman

Choo-choo Charlotte

Izzy Insomniac

I n the gingerbread factory
on Christmas Eve,
The night shift is cooking
Santa's candy to leave.
For stockings, for presents,
for St. Nick's own belly—
It's the sweets that he eats
that make it like jelly!

Sweet dreams! I'm helping myself to
a few goodies. Can you find me?
Then help me find Santa and these
workers in the gingerbread factory.

Lovely Louise

Fred Foreman   Clarisse Carpenter

Sarah Slacker   Sleepy Sam

Wesley Worker

Bill Boss   Quality Control Carol

On the night before Christmas,
Santa's elves are so busy,
Just watching them rush
    is making me dizzy!
I laughed as I watched them,
    in spite of myself—
It's hard to say which
    is the clumsiest elf!

The elves are in such a hurry, some
presents aren't coming out quite
right. Can you find Santa and me?
Can you find these odd presents?

An airplane

Roller skates

A stuffed animal

A tea set

A clock

A football

A doll

A hockey stick

A bicycle

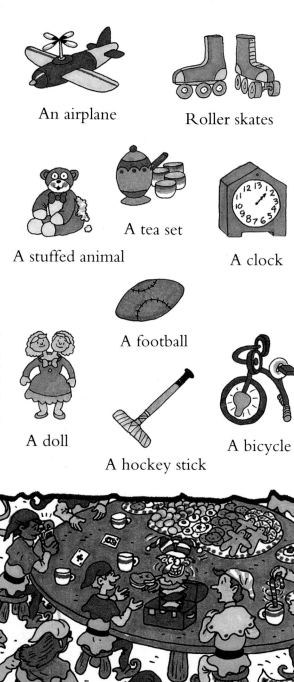

On the night before Christmas,
 every school has a party.
St. Nick is there, too,
 though he is a bit tardy.
He goes straight to work
 and starts filling up stockings—
The kids are still in 'em,
 and that's what's so shocking!

Can you find Santa and me as we
join in the good times? Can you
help me find these school things?

A ruler

A notebook

A stapler

A blackboard

A desk

Glue

A box of crayons

A globe

’Twas the night before Christmas,
  when all are asleep.
They’re snug in their beds
  and they’re counting their sheep.
Santa shouts as his sleigh
  disappears out of sight,
“Merry Christmas to all,
  and to all a good night!”

It’s getting late, and I’m still stirring!
Can you find me and Santa? Then
help me find these bedtime things.

A bedtime story

A Rudolph nightlight

A nightgown

A nightcap

A pair of fuzzy slippers

A teddy bear

A toothbrush

Six sheep for the children to count

People sure are spending a lot of money in the mall this Christmas Eve. Go back to the shopping mall and find these things that have to do with money.

☐ Dough
☐ Bread
☐ A buck
☐ George Washington
☐ A piggy bank
☐ A "charge"
☐ Big "Bills"
☐ An automatic teller

Bundle up and go back to the ice rink. Can you spy these chilly items?

☐ A cool cat
☐ "Ice" spy
☐ A snow shoe
☐ A polar bear
☐ Cold cash
☐ A giant snowflake
☐ Cold feet
☐ A cold turkey

Did you find the city folks in the crowded streets of downtown? Now look for these Christmas sights in the city.

☐ The Three Wise Men
☐ The Nutcracker
☐ The Little Drummer Boy
☐ A partridge in a pear tree
☐ Elves doing some Christmas "rapping"
☐ Mrs. Claus
☐ Mistletoe
☐ A shepherd

Let's go back to the zoo. Did you ferret out all the party animals? Can you spy (with your eagle eye) my other animal friends?

☐ A rattlesnake
☐ A wolf in sheep's clothing
☐ An owl and a pussycat
☐ A big fish in a small pond
☐ A pack rat
☐ Birds of a feather
☐ Reining cats and dogs
☐ Bats in the belfry